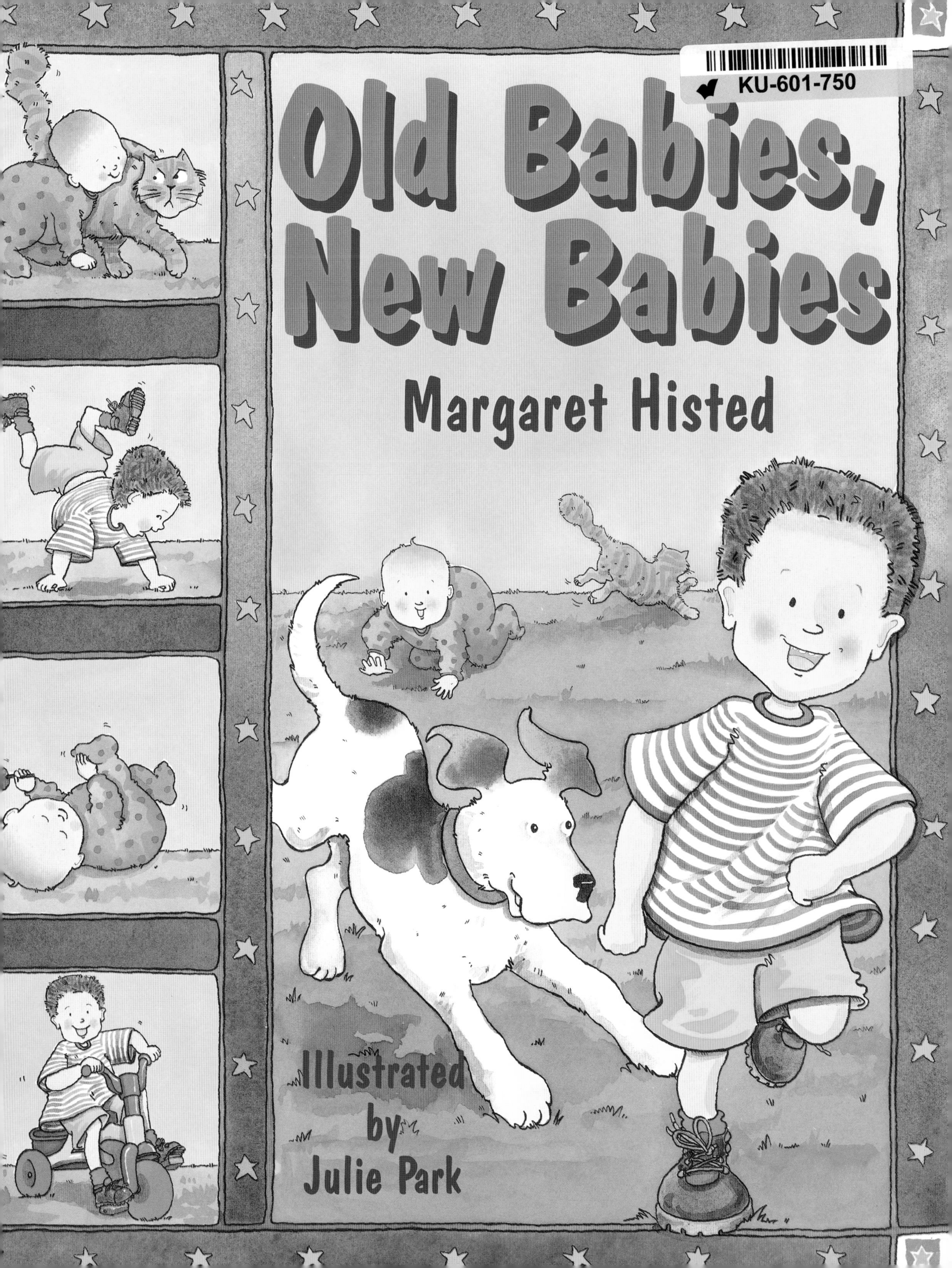
Old Babies, New Babies
Margaret Histed
Illustrated by Julie Park
KU-601-750

Josh and his mum were having breakfast when the phone rang. Mum went to answer it. When she came back, she sat down next to Josh and smiled at him.

Hello!
0
1
2
3
4
Ted
5
OOW!
6
7
8
9
10
Peepoo

For my children,
Tabby, Amy, Tom and Ashley,
with love, M. H.

First published in the United Kingdom in 1999 by Ragged Bears Publishing Limited, Milborne Wick, Sherborne, Dorset DT9 4PW

Distributed by Ragged Bears Limited, Ragged Appleshaw, Andover, Hampshire SP11 9HX. Tel: 01264 772269

A CIP record of this book is available from the British Library

ISBN 1 85714 148 2

Printed in Singapore

“Josh,” she said, “Sue and Dave have got a new baby. Isn’t that nice?”
Josh put his spoon down. He thought hard.

Sue and Dave used to live next door, but they had moved house in the summer. They already had a baby. She was called Laura.

FRAGILE
Come on Humpty......!
Wah! Wah!

Josh and Mum often used to visit next door. The mums would chat and Josh would watch Laura playing with her toys.

She could crawl quite fast and even stand up for a bit if she held on to something,

but she couldn't walk.

She couldn't talk either.

She was only a baby.

Josh wondered where Laura was now.
He tried to work it out, but it was difficult.

When Dad had bought a new bike, he had put an advertisement in the paper and a lady had come to the house and bought the old one.

No!

When Mum bought her new magazine every week, she always put the old one in the box under the sink, ready to go to the recycling centre.

Lupin! No! No!
No..No... Loopy.... No! .....Mummy!!

When Josh got a new jacket, Mum had given the old one to Sue, for Laura to wear when she was big enough.

Laura was only a baby. If Sue and Dave had got a new baby now, what had they done with their old one? What had they done with Laura?

rdrobe
0: half
able £20
draughtsman

nd Lorus
Bell Street
4) 455 578
matching
on - back
s with fire
rs (01374)

HER'S DAY
ks Nurseries
th February
n - 3p.m
dling the
2.67 each
Road

Soft
01189)

Articles For Sale

ALMOST NEW DOUBLE BUGGY with raincover £60. - (0148) 943350

ANTIQUE BRASS FENDER , 6ft X 15ins £270. - Telephone (01340) 704110

Baby For Sale

Laura, baby girl, 13 months old.
Fair hair, blue eyes, nearly walking.
Likes chocolate pudding, tickles and cats. Dislikes, wet nappies, bedtime and raisins. HAPPY HOME REQUIRED
Telephone Sue or Dave - (01731) 3085
Reason for sale, new baby arrived

H LOGS, plus ash, seasoned split
one (01492) 67

ELEC
£45 O.
Henle
EXHAU
delivery
Newtown
512674
FOR SA
makes
Hitach
Visit ou
Cententa
Road, He
G IS FOR
Get your

GAS FO
Butan
daily

GRA
Mar
Ke

ZZZZZ
Oh.... it's lovely Dot
I've knitted one in every colour of the rainbow...
Wah! Wah!
giggle giggle gigg

The next day, Josh and Mum went to visit the new baby. Mum had brought a present in her shopping bag.

When they got to Sue's house, the first thing Josh saw was Laura.

She was standing in the hallway, and when the visitors came in she toddled off to the living room and stood next to the pram, holding on to the side.

Mum tiptoed up to the pram. She said, "Hello, Laura! Is that your new baby?"

And Laura smiled and said, in a little voice, "Amy!"

Then she unwrapped the parcel Mum had brought.

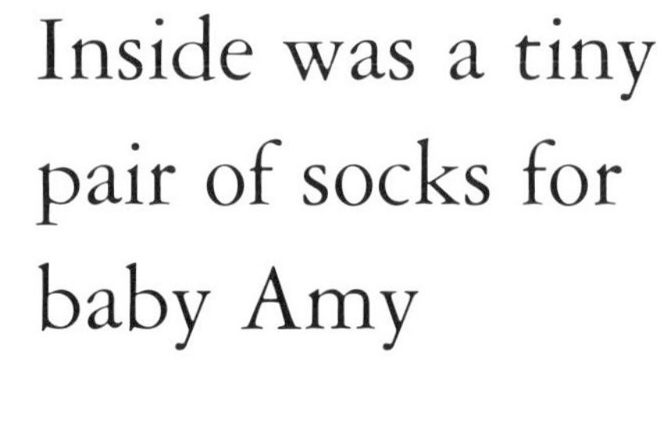

Inside was a tiny pair of socks for baby Amy

and a bigger pair of socks for Laura.

When they got home, Josh asked Mum why Laura was still at Sue's house. Mum didn't know what he meant,

so he explained all about new things and old things - about Dad's bike and the jacket and the magazines. Then Mum understood.

She lifted Josh on to her lap and gave him a big hug.
"Old babies don't go away when there are new ones,"
she said. "They get to be big brothers and sisters, even
if they are quite small like Laura.
That's how families grow."

They went to sit by the window. It was half-past three and lots of children were walking home from school with their families. As they sat together, Josh and Mum counted all the old babies and new babies they could see.